Edition Schott

Organ · Orgel

Naji Hakim
* 1955

Toccata

„Rottenburg Toccata"

über den Choral „Sankt Martin, dir ist anvertraut"

für Orgel
for Organ
pour orgue

ED 22524
ISMN 979-0-001-16061-2

www.schott-music.com

Mainz · London · Berlin · Madrid · New York · Paris · Prague · Tokyo · Toronto
© 2016 SCHOTT MUSIC GmbH & Co. KG, Mainz · Printed in Germany

Commissioned by the diocese of Rottenburg-Stuttgart for the St. Martin's anniversary year 2016

First performance:

8 November, 2015,
Rottenburg Cathedral (Germany),
by Professor Ruben Sturm

Preface

The Rottenburg Toccata develops the choral melody of "Sankt Martin, dir ist anvertraut" in the virtuosic style of french romantic toccatas. The work is articulated in three sections with contrasted textures: opening variation of the melody with sextuplet figurations, middle variation with a peasant rhythmical character in the minor mode and conclusion presenting the choral melody on the pedal.

Vorwort

Die Rottenburg Toccata entwickelt die Choralmelodie „Sankt Martin, dir ist anvertraut" im virtuosen Stil von französischen romantischen Toccaten. Das Werk gliedert sich in drei Abschnitte mit gegensätzlichen Texturen: eine eröffnende Variation der Melodie mit Sextolen-Figurationen, eine mittlere Variation mit ländlichem rhythmischen Charakter in Moll und einen abschließenden Teil, der die Choralmelodie im Pedal präsentiert.

Naji Hakim

Choralmelodie: *Sankt Martin, dir ist anvertraut*, Text: Ernst Hofmann und Hans Starz, Melodie: Johann Leisentrit 1567

Rottenburg Toccata
über den Choral „Sankt Martin, dir ist anvertraut"

Naji Hakim
* 1955
Melodie:
Johann Leisentrit 1567

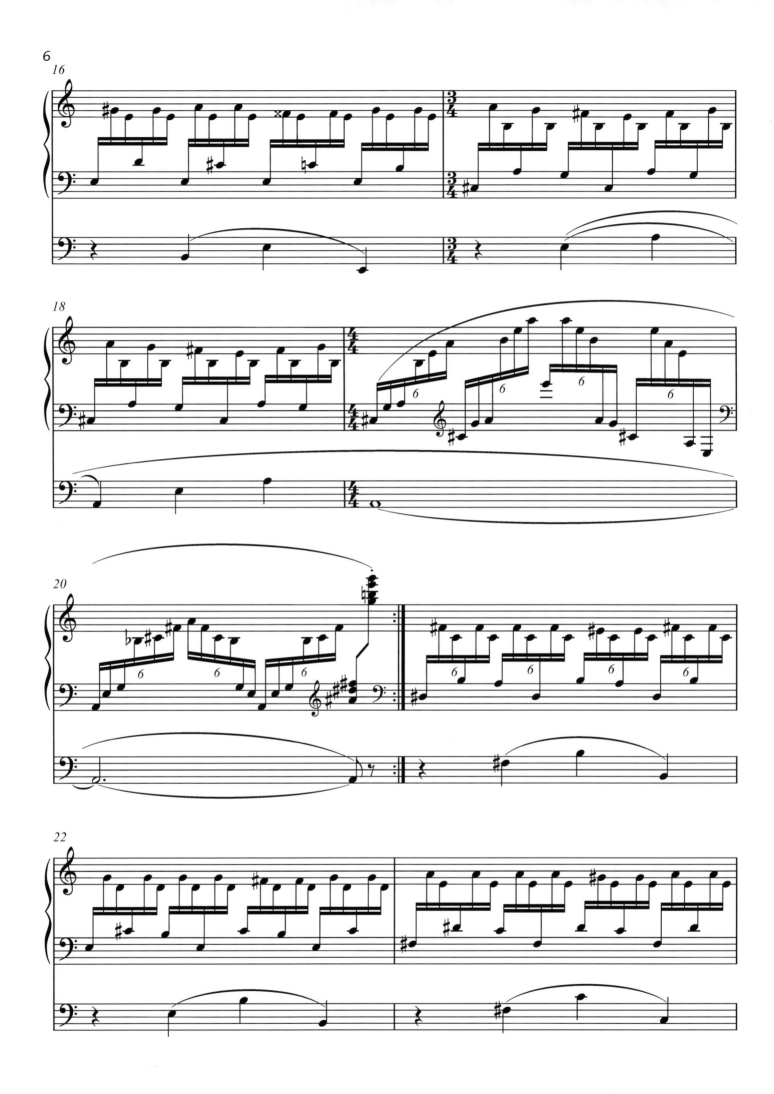

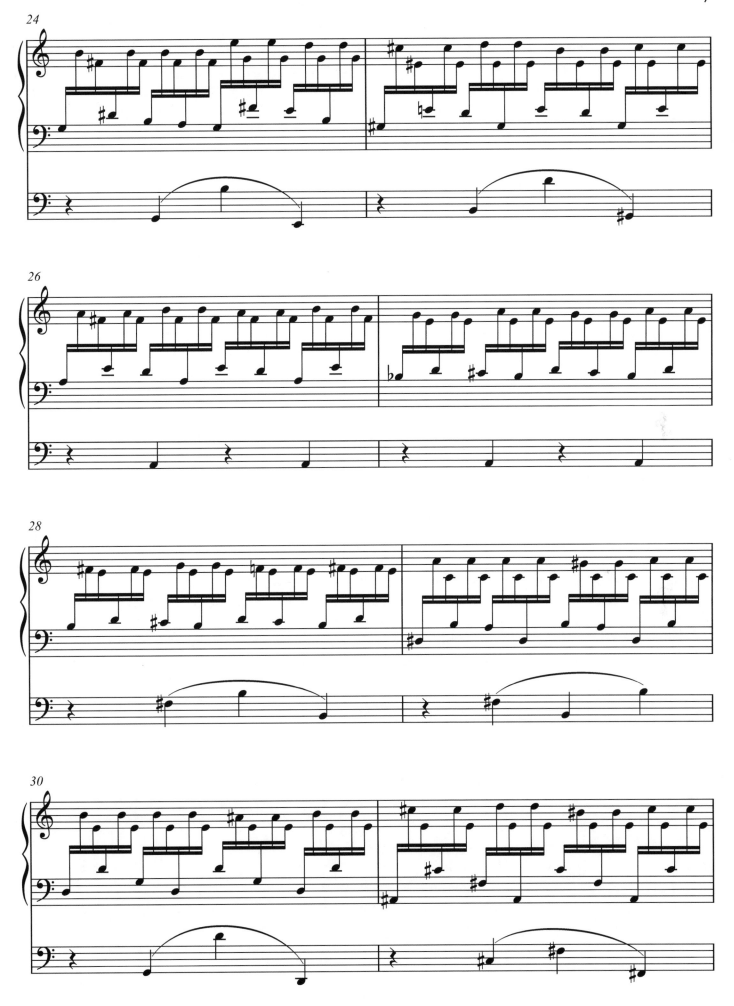